My Difference Is My Superpower

By E. A. Sim

Young Author Academy

BECOME A PUBLISHED AUTHOR

"My Difference is my Superpower," published through Independent Author Publishing.

Young Author Academy

Dubai, United Arab Emirates

www. youngauthoracademy. com

ISBN: 9798759785088

Printed by Amazon Direct Publishing.

This book was lovingly created by author E. A. Sim,
editor Aalia Thobani, illustrator Marta Morgan,
and publisher Annemieke Woodbridge.

Through the writing process, we learned that each of
our differences creates strengths,
which we illustrated in this book.

The characters were inspired by friends with learning
differences. They were interviewed as part of the
author's research process.

As you read this book,
we hope you realize your own superpower!

Hi, my name is Dyslexie.

I am nine years old and in the third grade.

I live in Sao Paulo, Brazil.

I enjoy drawing, painting,

photography, and creative writing.

I have so much fun going on

mountain hikes with my friends.

3

When I was eight years old,

my parents and teachers realized

I had a hard time reading books.

One year ago, I was diagnosed with dyslexia.

Dyslexia is a learning difference that makes it difficult to

read words, letters, numbers, and other symbols.

My Differences

I have a weak vocabulary and do not know
the meaning of a lot of words.

It is almost impossible for me to copy notes from
the board. I often write down information
from the wrong section.

I have a hard time reading small words in paragraphs.
The words tend to blur into each other.

My Superpowers

I am creative. When I read, I visualize pictures in my head. This expands my imagination.

I am inventive. My differences have taught me to read in different and unique ways. For example, I enjoy listening to audiobooks.

I am motivated. I have to work harder in the classroom than anybody else. Every time I read, I have to try my best to improve my reading skills.

Hello, I am Dyscallie.

I am seven years old and in the first grade.

I live in Petra, Jordan.

I am very athletic. I love to run, row, play beach volleyball, and rock climb.

I also enjoy baking pastries, cakes, and cookies.

Throughout my childhood, my teachers realized how hard it was for me to count, add, and solve math problems.

Two months ago, I was diagnosed with dyscalculia. Dyscalculia is a learning difference that makes solving math problems, and anything related to numbers, difficult to understand.

My Differences

I am often late to class and events because it is difficult for me to read the time.

In everyday life, it is tricky for me to understand the score in sports games, calculate prices at supermarkets, and figure out the tip at restaurants.

Many children with dyscalculia have math anxiety. Math anxiety makes you feel very stressed when you solve problems related to numbers and math.

I do not feel as confident as my friends in math class. However, I know that just because math is hard for me, it does not mean that I am not smart.

My Superpowers

I have learned to find an awesome support system.

My differences have taught me to ask teachers,

students, parents, and friends for help.

This has made me feel confident.

I am a strategic student who uses imaginative thinking

in math. For example, I use M&Ms to help me count

and map out word problems.

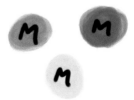

I am a star in speaking, reading, and writing.

Finding my areas of strength has helped me develop
a strong connection to words.

17

Hi there, my name is Dysgraphel.

I am eleven years old and in the sixth grade.

I recently moved to Venice, Italy

from Tokyo, Japan.

I enjoy water and snow sports. I love to

play water polo, ski, ice skate, and go sledding with my friends.

When I was in the third grade, my English teacher realized that I had a hard time writing.

Two years ago, I was diagnosed with dysgraphia.

Dysgraphia is a learning difference that negatively impacts handwriting, typing, and spelling skills.

My Differences

It takes me longer than other students to spell properly,

space out my words, and express my thoughts on paper.

When I write short stories,

my grammar is often incorrect.

My handwriting is hard to read and unclear.

My fingers don't stay in the correct position for a long time.

My Superpowers

I am great at tying my shoe-laces, typing, and coming up
with imaginative ideas for fictional stories.

I use cool technology like 'Dragon Naturally Speaking'
to speak my ideas into a microphone.

I have come up with new strategies to help me succeed in the
classroom. My planner helps me complete my work on time.

I attach pencil grips onto my writing utensils
to help me improve my hand position.

One Strength We All Share is Empathy

Our challenges have taught us to be kind
and understanding of everyone.

We appreciate our own strengths and those of others.

We have learned to see the good in every situation.

Our academic challenges have made us resilient.

We have held our heads high when bullied for our differences.

Our experiences have inspired us to help other children
who are not accepted for their unique qualities.

26

We Are Superheroes

We all have amazing strengths that will help us
make our mark on this world.

We want to use our voices through creative writing to
help celebrate other spectacular children like us.

What Is Your Superpower?

_____

_____

_____

About the Author
E. A. Sim

E. A. Sim grew up in New York City, Seoul, and Dubai and now lives on Long Island, New York. She rows for her high school's crew team and is a member of S.T.A.R., a student-led club that promotes mental well-being. She enjoys creative writing, surfing, and traveling all over the world.

E. A. Sim has interned at the Nicholas Center in Port Washington, New York, a center that provides vocational pathways for autistic adults.

She plans to work in the field of human development as a child psychiatrist or speech pathologist. Through her writing, she hopes to advocate for people with developmental challenges, neurological differences, and atypical backgrounds.

Made in the USA
Middletown, DE
21 December 2021

56793963R00020